Dedicated to

ALL THE YOUNG MEN of the plain churches in America.

May you find grace and strength to walk in the truth of our Lord Jesus Christ.

Acknowledgments

A SPECIAL THANKS TO:

My wife, Ethel, who made a huge contribution to this book. She spent many days rooting out my clumsy mistakes, and fleshing out paragraphs and pages that were too short and clipped. She also tediously corrected grammar and punctuation, and was a tremendous help and encouragement.

Marvin Yoder (author of the book *Draft Information Manual*), and Aaron Martin (who served on a draft Board for Selective Service System) for their time and efforts in helping make this book as correct and realistic as possible.

James Headings for his advice, and hours of editing work.

All others who have helped in any way, "God bless you."

Foreword

THIS BOOK INVOLVES MAJOR calamities and wars. It is about young men that experience the realities of war and draft times, including the encounter of the draft board face to face.

By writing this book I do not want to leave the impression that this country will soon be confronted with a major attack or war. I don't know any more about what other countries or people are planning than many of you do. Nor do I know of any plans to enact a draft any time soon.

So why bother with a book like this? I am involved with the *Conservative Anabaptist Service Program (C.A.S.P., a division of Christian Aid Ministries)* who is actively making preparations to provide suitable employment for Conscientious Objectors (CO's) in times of a draft. In talking to various church groups about this work, several concerns surface regularly.

These concerns could be summed up like this. **"What will our government be requiring of our boys?"** And, **"Will our boys be able to get a CO status?"**

The above questions are valid. The concerns are also valid. These questions and concerns need to be addressed.

C.A.S.P. has published a *Draft Information Manual.* That book covers the first question quite well, and is available from *Christian Aid Ministries.*

This book is an attempt to answer both questions in a book that depicts scenarios that are as they could happen in real life. I have attempted to set all scenarios as the military and draft laws are known at this time. All the happenings in this book are the carrier to help you, the reader, find the answer to the above questions.

The church community and the people involved in this book do not exist. And some countries are named that do not exist.

Some of the scenarios were patterned after things that actually happened to young men in the past.

The draft board scenes are given as we expect they may be. Some research was done in this area, but reliable information on this is somewhat limited, and laws can change.

In certain cases things happened that were shocking or scary. Our intention is not to shock and scare to create a sensation, only to help us face reality.

The burden and the concern that caused this book to be written is not about wars and facing draft boards; it is much deeper and much more important than that. The burden is the concern we have for the young men; young men that must give an account for themselves.

–Lyle Hostetler

Contents

The Struggles of Youth

"I DON'T KNOW HOW our country will react to all this." The feed salesman sat down on a stack of feed bags. "North Bab (a fictitious country) seems to be a powder keg almost ready to explode."

His words caused nineteen-year-old Ed to look up with a disturbed look. "What do you mean?"

"Just what I said. North Bab is very upset at the United States. And we don't need another war breaking out right now. Especially not here in the states."

"Do you actually think another war is brewing?"

"I don't know. But it looks to me like there's a pretty good chance that we'll see one before too many more years go by."

Ed had a troubled look on his face as the salesman drove out the lane, some time later.

Around the supper table that evening the conversation was lively as usual with everyone trying to relate the happenings of the past day. All but Ed. He sat in silence, barely hearing what the others were saying, surrounded by his own troubled thoughts.

"Ed, how was your day?" Mother looked inquiringly at her son. "You have been unusually quiet tonight."

Ed stirred in his seat, bringing himself back to the real world. Clearing his throat he started in, "Well, Prairie Feeds sent out their new feed salesman today."

"Oh? So, what did he have to say?" Dad looked up with interest, munching on a carrot.

"He didn't have much to say about our cattle; he was too wrapped up with what is happening in the different wars going on in the world," Ed answered, rather slowly.

"Are there some new developments, or why is he so concerned?" Dad queried, a puzzled look crossing his face.

"I don't really know, but he seems worried about North Bab and what they might do," Ed answered.

"He says the U.S. has her hands full enough without another conflict right now."

Dad's face turned sober. "We sure hope and pray that nothing like that will happen. But if it does we believe we have a God who is able to take care of us."

Ed mused over Dad's answer while he passed the meat platter to his sister. There was one other thing that hung heavy on his mind; so heavy that he could hardly make himself voice it. It had troubled him all afternoon.

"Dad, do you think the U.S. will start a draft any time soon?" he finally blurted out.

Dad chewed his food, silently ruminating over his son's question. Now he understood why Ed had been so quiet.

"No, son, I don't think so," he answered slowly. "Public sentiment is totally against the idea of a draft and our government is very sensitive to what the people think. I just don't think they would do it, even though they obviously need more troops."

Thus the subject was dismissed, but somehow Ed couldn't quite get it out of his mind. As he lay in bed that night watching the dancing shadows of a car passing by on the road, the words of the feed salesman kept running through his mind.

*   *   *   *   *   *   *   *

Ed headed for the house with Scott, his Border collie dog, right on his heels. He had finished the evening chores in record time. With eager steps he hurried to the house.

Living in Phelps County, Nebraska, Ed knew the sunset was still hours away. A long but pleasant summer evening awaited him and the other youth boys who were planning a baseball game that evening. Since this was a rare happening, it seemed extra special to Ed.

An hour later, Ed found himself in the middle of a lively game. The side he was on was trailing by two runs, but it looked like they had a good chance to catch up.

As Ed was sitting behind the backstop, waiting his turn to bat, he vaguely heard some boys behind him talking in low tones. Suddenly his ears perked up.

"How do you like that new DVD player you bought last week?"

Ed recognized his friend Jim's voice. *What is going on?* He listened in shocked surprise.

"Just great! I can hardly believe what some of those

girls do in those movies." Ed cringed as he heard Eli's flippant reply.

"Well, I could hardly believe about the girls in town either," Jim replied dryly.

"What are you talking about!?" Eli's voice rose a notch.

"I've been seeing a few of them now and then," drawled Jim.

"Ed! Batter up!" Ed jumped to his feet, ending the unintentional, but disturbing eavesdropping.

Later as Ed was driving home, his mind whirled dizzily. *Jim and Eli! I would never have thought . . . .* As he drove homeward, he barely noticed the loveliness of the evening. His thoughts were busy traveling back over the last year. Suddenly his own sins rose before him. *Why should it surprise me so much what Jim and Eli are doing? Is it because I am doing things I know I shouldn't? What would my parents think if they knew? What about the church? What about God? What if I were suddenly killed?* Ed groaned within himself. The weight of his past sins pressed heavily on his heart. *Oh, why do I go on?*

. . . .

After a long winter, spring finally arrived, but the spring was gone from Ed's steps. Ed was troubled as he plodded wearily toward the house one evening. Would he ever again have peace in his soul?

"Could you come with me to my office?" Ed started as his father met him at the door. One look at his dad's face told Ed there was something brewing. He didn't know what it was but somehow he didn't care. The burden of the last six months was almost more than he could carry anymore. His shoulders sagged as he nodded, silently following Dad into his office.

Settling down in the only other chair in the office Ed glanced anxiously at his dad. The love and kindness he saw mirrored in those trusting eyes caused him to drop his own.

"Son," Dad spoke softly. "Is something bothering you? Can I help in some way?"

Ed's eyes filled. *So he has noticed! What should I say? . . .*

"Ye-es, I guess there is," he finally stammered.

"Would you like to tell me about it?"

"Dad, I've been bad, a hypocrite—and I'm tired of it!" Ed finally blurted out.

"Tell me, son," Dad prodded. "Tell me what you

have done."

Ed knew it was now or never. He longed for peace in his soul once more. He was so tired of going around with this dreadful feeling in his heart. So Ed told his dad everything—every little detail.

When he finally finished, Dad sat with bowed head in stunned silence. To Ed it seemed like a long time. Then he slowly raised his face. Their eyes met.

"Son, I'm very sorry. I have failed you. I should have sensed your struggles and helped you a long time ago. But I thank God from the bottom of my heart for your repentance!" Dad laid his hand on his son's shoulder and they wept together.

.   .   .   .

The sun was high in the sky. It was Sunday morning and church services were almost over. Bishop Joseph Hostetler rose to make some announcements.

"We are saddened to say that we have a young brother that has fallen into sin. But we rejoice that he has come to us, confessed his sins and is wanting to make restitution. We will give our young brother time for his confession now."

Ed rose to his feet. *How can I say it . . .?* Panic struck, and he felt like running for the door. With faltering words he started in, "I have failed in my Christian life, sinning against God and the church. I have . . . ." He spilled it all out.

Ed sat down amid total silence. There were tears in Bishop Joseph Hostetler's eyes as he spoke again. "God bless you, Ed. I believe that there is great rejoicing in heaven just now. The Bible tells us that the angels rejoice when a sinner repents. Now I would like to ask our members to rise if you wish to show your love and forgiveness to our brother."

From the sounds coming from around him, Ed knew he was surrounded with compassionate friends.

"Thank you." Joseph Hostetler returned to his seat and someone announced a closing hymn.

After church Ed walked to his parent's car. *I feel as light as a feather. Why didn't I do this a long time ago?*

•   •   •   •   •   •   •   •

The stalks of corn disappeared steadily from the bottom of the combine's corn head. Ed was enjoying these fall days to the fullest. Running the combine gave him an opportunity to do some deep thinking. *This has been a good summer —the best I've had for a long while. But, oh, the old temptations—they are still so very real.*

The tractor and grain buggy appeared with Dad driving. As the last of the corn flowed into the wagon, Dad drove off with a friendly wave.

Dad! There is no one like him! It seems he has forgiven me completely. If I could only forget more easily.

Several weeks later found Ed and his father working in their Auto Repair Shop which was kept open for business except during their busy times on the farm. A sharp wind whistling around the store reminded them that winter had arrived.

As Ed worked he noticed the Phelps County Sheriff talking in the office with Dad. This wasn't unusual as they serviced all the sheriff department's vehicles on a regular basis. Yet it seemed their conversation sounded a little more serious than normal and the sheriff was staying longer than Ed expected.

That evening at the supper table Ed's curiosity got the best of him. "Dad," he queried, "did the sheriff have anything special on his mind today?"

Dad slowly chewed his food before answering. "Yes, he sure did." Then he took another bite of the buttered bread he was holding. It seemed he was stalling for time.

"Dad, is it something we did?" Mom questioned nervously.

"No. Well, maybe not exactly anyway. The sheriff was very vocal about his concern about world conditions. He thinks our military is really good at what they do but right now they are stretched so thin . . . It seems he has concerns that some of the other countries may notice this and take advantage by attacking us or some of our allies. He feels very strongly that we need to be drafting more men to serve in the military."

"Maybe he is just talking. I sure hope the draft isn't that near," Mom spoke consolingly. "We don't hear much about it."

"Well, he has unearthed some troubling thoughts in my mind," Dad continued, his face serious. "Somehow during our conversation when I mentioned the word "CO", it stirred him considerably. He told me quite vehemently, 'We know the boys from your church quite well. We know some of them are carousing around town in the evening. We also know some of them are renting dirty movies. Are you telling me these boys are Conscientious Objectors? Those boys aren't CO's! If I know anything about it, they will be going directly to the Army!'

"I was stunned!" Dad breathed heavily as he glanced at his son and saw the effect it had on Ed.

"Wha-at did you tell them?" Ed stammered, his face turning pale.

"I didn't answer him. I didn't know what to say."

"Oh, how terrible!" whispered Mom. "What can we do?"

Again the table was silent, the food on their plates completely forgotten.

"I think I had better go talk to our bishop sometime soon," Dad finally spoke again. "We must think about our boys. Our boys have a never-dying soul. We know that if they are drafted and they are denied the CO status as our sheriff thinks, they will either go to the military or they could face a large fine and a long prison sentence."

A few days later Ed questioned Dad. "What did our bishop think of what you had to say?"

"It really shook him," Dad answered. "He said he will call a meeting with the rest of the ministry, and they will possibly talk with some of the boys. He considers it their duty to warn them, but he did seem to be shocked that something like this was going on. He also mentioned that some of the boys in the church seemed to lack spiritual maturity."

"I'm disappointed that the ministry wasn't aware of it. Although I must say, it took me by surprise too the first time I heard Jim and Eli admit to some of these things." Ed paused then went on, "I know I hid some things from them too." Tears stung his eyes and he quickly brushed them with his sleeve.

"Yes, Ed, I can understand that you might be disappointed in the ministry," Dad admitted. "But remember, they are also only human beings. Perhaps they don't want to be too quick to be suspicious."

"I suppose you are right," Ed sighed. Then a new thought struck him. "What do you think the sheriff thinks about me?"

"Son, I don't know what the sheriff thinks, but I know that God knows what is in your heart. If you will stay close to Him, He will never leave you nor forsake you."

∙ ∙ ∙ ∙ ∙ ∙ ∙ ∙

Another year passed. One evening during the last week in November the youth were gathered at one of the parents' homes to pick pecan meats out of the shell. Ed enjoyed the evening, visiting with his many friends. As he was leaving for home that night, he walked in the dark toward the neat row of parked vehicles. Then he noticed a few boys clustered around one of the cars. His ears perked up when he heard them talking.

"I may not have liked what he said too well, but he seemed to be concerned about me."

"Huh! Concerned? The preachers are just trying to scare us. That sheriff is nothing to be worried about. It seems the last while the ministry is just picking on us boys."

"I don't know," was the other boy's reply. "It seemed to me they are really more concerned about our souls than about what that sheriff said."

"Huh! I still think they shouldn't pick on us so much."

With a heavy heart, Ed ducked into his car and drove off.

News Flash! U.S. Under Attack!

ED STOMPED THE SNOW from his boots as he came in from doing the morning chores. The smell of bacon frying added to the hunger pangs that he had been feeling for the last hour or more.

Drying his hands on the towel he glanced into the kitchen. The bowl of steaming oatmeal, and the plate of bacon released a very fragrant aroma as he slid into his chair.

Ed reverently bowed his head as his father led in the morning prayer. Everyone dug in hungrily as the platters of food were passed around.

"Does anyone want more eggs or bacon?" asked Mom, lifting the platters invitingly.

"Yes, I'll take more of both," spoke up Ed.

"RING-G-G!"

"Here, pass this down to Ed while I go to the other room to answer the phone," Mother said, pushing her chair back.

A few minutes later she burst into the room, her face white as a sheet. "You can't believe what has happened!"

All eyes turned and were fastened on Mom's face.

"What *has* happened?" gasped Dad anxiously.

"They have bombed us! Someone bombed San City! It sounds horrible!"

Everyone was stunned into silence. Dad finally found his tongue. "How bad is it? Who did it?"

"That was Mrs. Johnson. She said when they turned on their TV this morning, they heard the shocking news. They said there are thousands dead, possibly hundreds of thousands!" Mom dropped into a chair, her color slowly returning. Gaining her composure, she repeated, "I just can't believe it. Right here in the U.S."

Later in the barn Ed found Dad and questioned him. "Dad, what will this do to me? Do you still think there won't be a draft?"

Dad looked at his son. He saw a worried expression written on Ed's face. "Son," Dad said slowly. "I don't know, but this may change everything. I expect we will know soon. In the mean time, we must pray— pray that God will grant us grace for whatever lies before us. It is all in His hand."

Several days later they received more news. "San City is still burning. North Bab is threatening even more destruction. Now the President has declared war against North Bab." Mom turned from the telephone with the dreaded news.

Dad spoke up first. "I was afraid of this. May God be merciful." A somber silence reigned over the family as the realization of her words sank in.

Ed numbly returned to his work, his mind in a whirl. *If there is a draft, will our government consider me a Conscientious Objector? . . . . What about my past?*

. . . .

The sun was peeping over the eastern horizon. The beautiful Nebraska sunrise went unnoticed as Ed made his way to the house and the waiting breakfast. He expected his dad to have made a phone call and he almost dreaded to hear what the news might be.

The family was seated around the table as he entered the house. The usual hum of voices was missing; everyone sat in solemn quietness waiting for Ed to take his place.

Ed quickly washed, then made his way to the table. Still silence reigned. Wordlessly Dad bowed his head and everyone followed suit. "Our kind and merciful Heavenly Father, we thank Thee for the many blessings of life. We thank Thee for the food that lies before us. Bless this food to the nourishing of our bodies and bless those that have prepared it. We pray for our country in this difficult time. We pray for the leaders of our land; help them and guide them. Lord, give us wisdom and strength for whatever we may need to face in the coming days. In Jesus' name we pray, Amen."

Quietly Dad reached for the bowl of steaming oatmeal. Ed could bear the silence no longer. He had to know.

"Dad, did you hear anything new about the situation in our country?"

Dad passed the bowl of oatmeal before answering. "Yes, I made a call this morning. The president has declared a National Emergency, and he is asking for the draft to be reinstated. Congress is to go into an emergency session this morning to ratify it."

A strange silence fell over the room as the news soaked in. All eyes were fixed on Ed. A cloud passed over his face as he asked, "Do you think Congress will pass it?"

"Yes," Dad answered, "they probably will. This country is really upset over these matters; defense and retaliation is on everyone's minds—sorry to say."

"Maybe Ed will draw a real high number; then he won't be called," one of his younger brothers spoke up hopefully.

"We certainly hope and pray that will be the case," Dad answered. "But if he is called . . . well, I have to think of Jesus in the Garden of Gethsemane when He prayed 'Let this cup pass from me,' but then He added in perfect submission, 'Not my will, but thine be done.' We think we know what we need but we really want to accept whatever God gives us."

Ed filled his plate, picking at his food for a few moments. Then he pushed his plate away. He simply had lost all desire to eat. He rose from the table and stumbled out the door heading for the barn. There he found his "secret closet."

News: Congress Ratifies War and Draft. U.S. Scrambles

THE NEXT MORNING ARRIVED uneventfully. In spite of the turmoil in the nation's capital, life on the farm went on almost as usual. Ed was feeding the cattle when he noticed Dad approaching. He had a grave look on his face. Ed shut off the tractor to hear what Dad had to say.

"They say Congress has passed a bill enacting the draft. The president issued an order to Selective Service to take emergency measures to implement the draft law as swiftly as possible."

Ed took the news in silence as he jumped from the tractor. It seemed like a heavy burden had suddenly descended on him. Leaning against the tire, he sighed heavily.

"Ed," Dad started in gently, "are you worried about what the draft board may decide about you?"

"Yes," Ed answered slowly. "I know my past. I figure they may know it too."

"Well, I expected you may be thinking along that line. This is a great concern for your mother and me, too. But we are so thankful for the change you have made and the sincerity we see in you the last six months. We also know that God is still on the throne. He rules and over-rules. Let's trust Him to be with us whatever may come." Dad's consoling council brought little relief to the troubled young man.

Long after Dad left, Ed's heart overflowed with emotions. On one hand was fear. Fear of the unknown. Fear of what might come. Fear of not being able to express what was in his heart to the draft board. On the other hand he felt so thankful, almost elated, that he had a father and mother that cared. He could feel their love for him, and their love for God. And, he knew God loved him too. What a merciful God he served!

* * * * * * * *

A somber youth group gathered for another "nut picking." The atmosphere had changed drastically from the summer before. What was usually a happy carefree time together, now had a sober note to it.

The news had traveled like wild-fire. The newspaper that day had an official announcement of the Draft Lottery Numbers for all the twenty-year-old boys from the Selective Service System. This notice officially assigned them their lottery number.

The newspaper announcement stated as follows: *Each day of the year is assigned a random number, from 1 to 365. Drafting will begin with the boys whose birth date have drawn number "1". The birth date assigned number "2" will follow and continue with ascending numbers until the need for soldiers is filled.*

A graph containing the numbers up to 365 and the corresponding birth dates was included.

They had known the announcement was coming, and everyone had hoped that each of the boys would get a high number. The high numbers would be the later ones to be called. They also knew that if the military needs were satisfied before the higher numbers were called, they would then be exempt from the draft.

When the newspaper was laid open it revealed that all but one of the twenty-year-old boys had fairly low numbers. Ed's number was "14." He was almost sure of being drafted if he passed the physical examination.

As the youth sat in a circle around the room the talk was subdued. "How many boys do we have that are twenty?" wondered one of the girls, flipping a nutmeat into the bowl.

"There are four," answered another. "But Earl has a real high number—over 300. He may not have to go, unless they really need a lot of men."

"My dad said if they *really* want a lot of men they will start to draft the 21-year-olds, and if that is not enough they will call the 19-year-olds. They could draft men all the way up to age 26."

"Oh! Let's hope it doesn't get that bad!" gasped another girl.

The girls worked in silence for several moments. Then a serious-looking young lady spoke up. "I wonder how our local draft board will react to our boys."

"I certainly hope they will be reasonable," stated another.

"My dad says he hopes they won't take the same attitude our sheriff did."

Over in the corner one of the boys spoke up. All eyes turned in his direction. It was Jim. "I think you are all making too big a thing about this. Those draft boards are nothing to be worried about. They know our church has been nonresistant for centuries. I am not a bit worried that I won't get a CO status!"

A slight titter of nervous laughter came from a few of the boys. But most of them had a serious look on their face.

Ed overheard the girls' talk. He wondered how much he should say. It was certainly embarrassing to talk about his past, especially in front of all these youth. Then he thought of the words of Jesus, "Whosoever shall be ashamed of me and of my words, of him shall the Son of man be ashamed."

Clearing his throat he started in, "I may be too scared. But you all know my past. There is a possibility that our draft board knows it too. When I stand before the draft board, I hope and pray, God will give me the wisdom to say the right words." He paused, then seeing the reaction it brought he hurried on, "Please pray for me that I may be faithful to God; if the draft board grants me a CO or if they deny it."

The Mail Arrives

ED WAS WATCHING FROM the repair shop window when the mailman stopped at the end of the lane. He dropped his work and almost trotted to the mailbox.

Sure enough, there was an envelope from **Selective Service System**—big and ominous. Ed tore it carefully across the end. Then he pulled out the contents.

SELECTIVE SERVICE SYSTEM

ORDER TO REPORT FOR ARMED FORCES EXAMINATION

Local Board/Area Office
Street Address
City, State, ZIP

SELECTIVE SERVICE SYSTEM
ORDER TO REPORT FOR ARMED FORCES EXAMINATION
(RIPS)

Date of Issuance 12-1-07

Registrant's Name   Selective Service Number
Street Address   Social Security Number
City, State, Zip   Random Sequence Number

This is your Order to report for and submit to an Armed Forces Examination for the purpose of determining your potential acceptability for military service.

You are hereby directed to report, with this Order, to: Holdrege, Nebraska Bus Station
                                                         (DESIGNATED ASSEMBLY POINT)
on   Dec. 8   at 6 a.m.   for transportation to the Military Entrance Processing Station (MEPS)
    (DATE)   **(TIME)**
in   Grand Island Nebraska
       (CITY AND STATE)

Upon completion of your examination, you will be returned to the place of reporting shown above.

If you are closer to the MEPS than to the place you are ordered to report, and if you wish to go directly to the MEPS, contact the Area Office shown above for instructions.

If you are so far from your Area Office that reporting in compliance with this Order would be a hardship, and if you wish to report to the Area Office where you are now located, contact that Area Office and request a transfer for examination.

You will be furnished transportation, and meals and lodging when necessary, from the designated place of reporting to the MEPS and return. It is possible that you may be retained at the MEPS for more than one day for the purpose of further processing. If you have any physical or mental condition which you believe may disqualify you for service, or if you are physically incapable of reporting to the MEPS, contact your Area Office for instructions.

If you believe you qualify for a postponement of your examination, complete the attached Request for Postponement of Armed Forces Examination (SSS Form 233P) and return it to your Area Office before the date you are scheduled to report.

Read the Important Information Sheet provided with this Order. If you fail to obey this Order you may be reported as a suspected violator of the Military Selective Service Act and, if convicted, subject to imprisonment for up to five years, a fine of up to $250,000, or both.

Director of Selective Service

Attachment

FOR INFORMATION AND ADVICE, CONTACT ANY SELECTIVE SERVICE AREA OFFICE.

SSS FORM 233

11-105

A-185

The color drained from his face as he read the letter. It was definitely short and to the point. They had wasted no words. *So this is it. The call that I've been dreading so long has come.* **The call of the Selective Service System!**

Ed slowly returned the contents into the envelope,

walking to the door of the office. As he pulled the door open and walked inside, Dad looked up from his work at the desk. His face spoke volumes as he noticed the important looking letter in Ed's hand. "What do you have?"

"This is it." Ed felt strangely calm as he handed the letter to his dad. "I guess you might say it's the call of the SSS."

Scanning the contents, Dad folded the letter thoughtfully. "It looks like they have made up their minds about what you will do. They are asking you to bring certain personal belongings as if you are going for a few days."

"What are they really saying?" Ed wondered aloud, even though he thought he knew. Somehow he needed to hear his dad say it.

"They are saying you must be ready to board the bus for Grand Island in 10 days." He opened the letter and read it once more. "You need to bring this and this and this—(pointing to the list of items in the letter), because you could be detained for the second day."

"Don't I even have a chance to tell them I am a nonresistant CO?" Ed looked worried.

"I think they will grant you that opportunity

sometime later. I hear they will probably send everyone a form to fill out and send in if they pass the medical and mental examination in Grand Island."

Ten days later, in the morning darkness, a group had gathered at the bus station, waiting for the bus. Most of the group were jovial. The talk among them ranged from coarse to vulgar.

Over to one side another group stood out, totally different. Their dress, speech, and conduct was different. They were also more sober. There were three sets of parents, and three boys. One of them was Ed.

The bus came to a screeching halt in front of the waiting group. The door opened and the driver called out, "All aboard for Grand Island!" With much jostling and shuffling the loading began.

Soon most of the boys were on the bus, all but the quiet group that stood off to one side. The parents murmured words of encouragement to their sons. Then they waved goodbye as the three boys stepped on the waiting bus. The bus was off with a roar amid a cloud of smoke.

* * * * * * * *

Ed cringed as he heard the uniformed man's harsh instructions. "Now listen closely! Along the wall on your left is a row of lockers. Find an empty locker and place your personal belongings inside, along with the clothes you are wearing except for your underwear, money and billfold. Place your billfold in the brown paper bag you find inside the locker. Take the key and lock the locker. Place the key in your paper bag, and write the locker number on your paper bag with the pencil that is in the locker. Then form a single file line along the right wall."

The young men tried to follow the orders, sometimes exchanging questioning glances when they were not sure how to do something. No one dared venture more than a short, whispered question.

By the time they had deposited their belongings and clothes inside the locker and found their place in the long line of young men along the wall, they felt as if they had left all their dignity in that tiny locker on the other wall.

The officer opened a door leading into another large room. "O.K. you slow pokes, get a move on!" he shouted loudly. "Step up to the line of men who will be taking blood samples. Follow orders exactly and there will be no trouble!"

Ed was close to the front of the line that filed toward the appointed door. He watched with interest as the young men in front of him filed through the door, then walked toward the two men in white gowns who were obviously the ones prepared to draw the blood samples.

The two men sat in chairs, one on each side of the aisle, each with a small desk with their syringes and needles, and other supplies.

When the first young man in the long line neared their side they rose in unison, as if rising to attack. They grabbed the syringes, holding them high above their heads, as if they were knives ready to stab. Their actions were that of a vicious attacker.

"Come here!" they shouted, their voices threatening.

The young man in front had more than he could take. He crumpled in a heap on the floor.

The men in white gowns doubled over in laughter. They had accomplished their goal. The young man who had fainted was drug off to the side like a dead dog. He was left to recover by himself.

"Next!" called the men in gowns. Their faces bore a silly smirk, but they seemed ready to go about their business in a more business-like manner.

Ed's turn was coming up. He glanced at the young man still lying on the floor close by. He was beginning to stir. As Ed extended his arm for the needle he felt a bit woozy. What an unsettling way to start the medical examinations! But somehow he made it through. As he moved to the next room with the line of subdued young men, he wondered what they would meet around the next corner.

All day long, orders were barked at them, almost in machine-gun fashion. What a long tiresome day it was!

Then they were ordered into a large room that looked a little like a school room. The medical examinations seemed to be over with, now they faced the written examinations.

They filed past a desk where an officer stood and passed out some papers and a pencil to each of them. They were given a few curt instructions and told to find a desk and complete the tests.

Ed settled into the first desk he found available and glanced at the large clock on the wall. He had a determination to get this behind him as soon as possible. The officer had announced the time deadline and Ed had no desire to tangle with him in any way.

Finally it seemed they were almost finished. Everyone was herded into the same room where they had started. Ed longingly eyed the lockers on the far wall. *I hope I can get my clothes soon. What a day!*

The loud speaker boomed again. "Everyone find his locker and get dressed. The buses are waiting outside to take you home. Look at the destination signs above the doors, and form a line for the bus that will take you home."

Without hesitation Ed headed for the lockers. He found his clothes and hurriedly dressed himself. Picking up his other belongings, he turned to leave. Then he discovered that Jim and Fred were right behind him. He gave them a weak smile, then walked toward the door that had a bus outside, waiting to return to Phelps County, Nebraska.

The ride back home was much quieter. The three boys from Ed's church sat deep in thought. By this time the whole crowd seemed more subdued.

"I wonder how long it will be until we know if we passed?" Ed mused looking at Fred in the seat beside him.

"I wonder too," answered Fred. "I suppose it will be a while. Usually the wheels of the Government move slowly."

Jim overheard their conversation from where he was seated across the aisle. He leaned halfway across. "I sure hope it doesn't take them more than a week! They say we have only ten days to prove we qualify as a CO once we are notified to appear for a hearing. It shouldn't take that long." He grinned at the other two. "I'm anxious to head for a hospital to work somewhere for my Alternative Service. I hear they have lots of pretty nurses." His wink brought no returning response from the other two.

Ed had nothing to say. He was not confident of his outcome. Neither was Fred. They had seen only a little bit of military life, and they had suddenly discovered how the world looked at them. They were also aware of some things that made them very uncomfortable.

The bus rolled on. It was Friday evening, the day was long gone. Lights flashed by the windows in the dark as they passed through a small country burg. Ed's mind was whirling. *What is my next step? I guess there is nothing to do now but wait for a letter in the mail.*

• • • • • • • •

During the next days, Ed watched the arrival of the mailman anxiously. From his window in the repair shop he could see when the mail carrier with its flashing lights came around the corner. As soon as it came to a halt at the mail box, Ed headed out the lane.

After following this ritual for almost a week he began to wonder if the letter would ever come.

One day when Ed and his dad were deeply involved in conversation with a customer, discussing the customer's car problems, Ed's dad happened to look out the window.

"Excuse me," Dad said politely. "I think Ed, you may have an errand to tend to."

Ed followed his dad's glance at the window in time to see the mailman pull away from the mailbox. "Oh! excuse me, I need to go." He headed out the lane at a run. *How could I have forgotten?!*

Running across the blacktop toward the mail-box he caught a flash of movement. He gasped as he faced the speeding car. "SCREEECH!" The tires smoked as the car headed straight toward him.

Ed leaped toward the mail-box. As the car skidded past it missed Ed by bare inches. The petrified look on the driver's face was etched into Ed's mind as his trembling hands reached for the mailbox. How could he have been so careless?!

Opening the mail-box he reached for the stack of mail. There on top lay an envelope with a return address. "**Selective Service System**" jumped out at Ed in bold letters.

Ed turned toward the house, tearing the letter open as he walked.

Hmm. Just as I figured. They say I am qualified . . . and it says I am classified 1-A. I guess they want me to be a part of their huge military machine.

He walked into the shop where he noted the customer getting ready to leave. As soon as the door closed behind him he handed the official looking letter to his dad.

"Well, what have we got here?" Dad asked, pulling the contents from the envelope.

"I think it's just what we expected," Ed answered. "They want me in the Army."

"Yes, I believe you are right. They have you down as a 1-A, which means you are now a part of the military, waiting for the call to report."

Dad kept thumbing the paper. "Oh, there is another paper here!"

He pulled it out, scanning the contents. "So this

is form 8. This is the form you may fill out when requesting to be reclassified."

Local Board/Area Office
Street Address
City, State, ZIP

SELECTIVE SERVICE SYSTEM
CLAIM FOR RECLASSIFICATION
(RIPS)

Date of Issuance 12-13-07

Registrant's Name and SSN   Social Security Number
Street Address   Random Sequence Number
City, State, Zip   Processing Number

Do we have your correct address? If not, cross out the incorrect information above and write in the correct information.

☐ If you made corrections to your address above, and if you wish to have your claim considered by the office nearest this new address, place a check in box.

PART I: CLAIM FOR RECLASSIFICATION

All claims for reclassification must be made at the same time. Check each statement below which applies to you, sign and date the form, and return it to the Area Office shown above within ten days from the date of issuance.

☒ Conscientious objector	State or federal elected public
___ CO discharge	official or judge of court of record
___ Hardship to dependents	___ Active military or uniformed service
___ Hardship discharge	___ Prior military or uniformed service
___ Ministerial student	___ Reserve or National Guard member
___ Minister of religion	(including ROTC)
___ Alien or dual national	___ Surviving son or brother

Do not send any supporting documents with this form to prove your claim. Your Area Office will contact you if any documents are needed and will provide instructions on where and when they should be forwarded.

PART II: STUDENT STATUS

☐ If you are not making a claim for reclassification, but are attending high school or college full time, place a check in box.

PART III: CERTIFICATION

I certify that the information I have provided on this form is true, accurate and complete to the best of my knowledge and belief.

Edward Martin   12-15-07
(Registrant's Signature)   (Date)

SSS FORM 8 (AUG 2000)

11-2

A-115

Ed edged closer to see the paper. "Oh, yes, that is what I want."

"I think we should call the ministry for some help. It seems important that you fill this out correctly," Dad advised.

"Maybe I will try to call Sam right now," Ed answered as he reached for the phone.

Deacon Sam Burkholder answered the phone on the second ring. "Hello, this is Sam."

"This is Ed," he returned. "I got my Notice of Acceptability today in the mail. They have classified me as 1-A, but they also included a form 8 in the letter."

"Oh, O.K.; I guess that is what we all expected isn't it?"

"Yes," Ed answered. "But I was wondering if you could help me fill this out. I would like to be sure to have it right."

"Sure, I will gladly help all I can," Sam responded helpfully. "That form is very simple though. I wonder if I can help you over the phone."

"If you think that is possible, it would be quite all right with me."

"Do you have the form in front of you?"

"Yes, I do."

"Do you see where it says, Part 1?"

"Yes, I see it," Ed replied.

"You want to file to be classified 1O, don't you?"

"Definitely!" answered Ed.

"Now, look in the column with "Conscientious

Objector" on the top. Put an X on the line in front of that."

"O.K., I see that."

The only other thing you need to do is sign and date it. Then mail it in."

The phone conversation ended with some friendly pleasantries, and Ed turned to face his dad.

"I hope all of this stuff is this easy," he grinned, his face relaxing somewhat.

"I wouldn't plan on that," Dad answered evenly. "We may still have some trials ahead of us."

Little did they know of what really lay ahead of them in the days and weeks to come.

Draft Board Hearings

CHURCH SERVICES WERE ALMOST over. A tone of extra seriousness hung over the congregation as their minister, Chester King, finished preaching a very thought-provoking sermon. Now, as Bishop Joseph Hostetler rose to make his announcements the people were listening with rapt attention. The draft was on everyone's mind.

"As you all know, our country is in a very difficult time. The president is doing his best to strengthen our defenses to ward off those who attack us. At the same time he is making plans for an all-out offensive attack. To do this he must have more soldiers.

"We have three young men that will appear before the local draft board this coming week and the next.

This is a very crucial time for these young men. They need our prayers. Tomorrow we want to have a day of fasting and prayer. We know that God can and does move men according to His will, but we are also aware of the possibility that we are the ones that need to be moved. Also, we as a ministry want to offer our help to these young brethren. We know there are forms to fill out, essays to write. They may want to choose some witnesses to go with them. We are limited in what we can do, but we can pray, and we will help where we can."

After church Ed waited in the parking lot. When the bishop stepped outside the church house Ed strolled over to him. "I am sure glad for your attention to the needs of us boys. I definitely want your help."

"We, as a ministry, really feel for you boys. I don't know how much I can help, but I certainly will try my best," responded Joseph with feeling.

"I noticed that the application form asks me to explain in writing what I believe and how I came to believe it. I am not a good writer at all, yet I know I must write it as I see it. But I thought maybe I could write it in my words then some of you could at least help make it more readable," said Ed.

"Chester is fairly good with words; maybe we can get him to help you with that," suggested Joseph.

"As far as witnesses, who do you think I should take along?"

Joseph thought a moment. "I think your Dad would be a good one."

"They say I can take up to three witnesses plus a counselor; would you go with me as my counselor?"

"I don't know how much good a counselor can do. But I will go with you if you like." Bishop Joseph smiled slightly.

"I appreciate that. Who would you suggest as my second witness?" Ed wondered.

Joseph studied in silence, then he suggested, "How about Bob Jerger from NAPA Auto Parts? You have a good relationship with him, don't you?"

"Well, I don't know," Ed hesitated. "Back when I was doing as I pleased he seemed to know all about it." A worried frown creased his brow.

"Does he seem aware that you have changed?"

"Well, maybe. He has mentioned lately that something has changed; he doesn't see me in town much anymore."

Again Joseph paused before he spoke. "Bob is well known as a solid, trusted businessman. He may be just the man you need."

"O.K., I'll ask him first thing in the morning. And could I meet with you the evening before the hearing to review everything?"

"Sure; and I will ask the others of the ministry to be there too. Maybe we can even rehearse some of the things they may confront you with to help you be somewhat prepared."

"I don't know if there is such a thing as being prepared. I feel like Daniel—ready to be thrown into the den of lions," Ed stated meekly.

Joseph answered, "I don't know what they will decide, none of us knows. Only God Himself knows the outcome of these sessions. But I do know that God is able to take care of us, just as He was able in Daniel's case."

. . . .

Tuesday morning arrived. "I hear Fred has also asked the ministry for help in preparing for his Draft Board hearing," Mom remarked as the family gathered for morning devotions. "But it really is sad the way Jim is determined to go on his own."

"What is sadder yet is the fact that Jim really has no good relationship with the ministry, and it makes us wonder how his relationship is with God. Could it be any better? Yet it seems he hopes to escape the military duty somehow," Dad added, his face sober.

"I heard someone make the remark, 'Jim is a good talker.' He might somehow talk his way through," Mom put in.

"I'm afraid words won't hold much water in this case," Dad said sadly.

"Dad, what would happen if someone just refused to go to the hearing, or to the military?" Ed questioned.

"I hear there are some in other churches that are considering that," Dad answered. "But I question the wisdom of it. The possible penalty for that is up to five years in prison and a $250,000.00 fine. I suppose the court would decide on the severity of the penalty."

"Isn't there a good chance that the court would give a much lesser penalty?" Ed asked. "That seems pretty severe."

"Yes, there is a chance," Dad answered. "But knowing how upset the people are around here, it seems to me the chances of a merciful sentence might be pretty slim, and the influences of prison life can be very undesirable."

"Dad, I am determined that if the draft board rules against me I will take whatever sentence I am given."

. . . .

"What about Fred?" Deacon Sam Burkholder asked the others in the ministry. "I talked to him today, and I must say I was disappointed. It seems he is scared stiff about what they may ask him to do. But he really has very little knowledge of why we don't go to war, and doesn't seem to care a whole lot about it. He just wants us to tell him what to say."

Joseph sighed loudly. "I have suspected as much about Fred for the last while. Until now we had no proof. Now it may be too late."

Several days later found Fred walking into the hearing room at the local courthouse. The three men of the local draft board sat in a row along the far side of the long table. There was a lone chair on the opposite side.

"Are you Fred Yoder?" The tall man sitting in the center looked sternly over his glasses.

"Yes, I am," answered Fred meekly, trying to quiet his thumping heart. When he looked into the face of the man he suddenly felt weak in the knees. *This man is John, the manager of the local Pizza Hut!*

"Be seated," the man ordered gruffly, motioning to the lone chair opposite him. Deacon Sam Burkholder and Fred's father stood along the wall behind Fred.

"Who is Fred's counselor?" the tall man asked. He seemed to be the spokesman for the draft board.

"I am," stated Sam.

"Very well, you may sit beside Fred if you wish. You may also advise him at times, but you may not interfere with the hearing process. You may not speak to us unless we ask you. And if we ask you, you must speak."

Sam took his place.

The tall man spoke again. "I am John, and I am the chairman of this board. Any member of the board is free to ask questions."

"Fred, I take it you brought your father as a witness?" John asked.

"Yes, sir," Fred answered.

"You may stay where you are, and you may not speak unless spoken to," John directed Fred's father. "This won't take too long. We are expected to conduct this hearing in twenty minutes or less."

John picked a paper from the stack in front of him. He eyed Fred sharply. "So Fred, just what makes you think you should be a CO?"

Fred was at a loss for words. This was so unexpected, and from John!

"I, I, don't know. I, I, am a Mennonite and we don't go to war," he finally managed to stammer.

"Oh, so you are a Mennonite and you don't go to war," John raised his voice. "I know you claim to be a Mennonite, and I know you claim to dress like a Mennonite, but you sure don't dress and comb yourself like your dad. So why should I think you believe like your dad? —Or your church for that matter?!"

"But I believe I should be nonresistant, so I couldn't go to war," Fred stated rather desperately, trying to think of a way to calm this man.

"Oh, I see," John sneered. "So you are nonresistant."

Now the man at the far right spoke up. "I see on your records you had a speeding ticket about a year ago—78 miles per hour in a 55 mile per hour speed zone. The record also shows you made quite a protest. Was this protest because you are *nonresistant*?" he mocked.

Fred sat for a long moment in stunned silence. *What all do they know about me?*

John eyed Fred sharply. "Are you nonresistant in the same way your dad is?"

"Yes," answered Fred, relaxing a little, thinking he was finally on the right track.

"Okay," challenged John sternly. "Your dad dresses in a manner that is fairly consistent with the rest of your church, yet the records show that three years ago your dad used the small claims court to collect a debt of $1694.00. Is this an act of nonresistance? Or are you claiming to be nonresistant only in time of war? Answer me!"

Fred was stupefied into silence. *What can I say?* "I, I, I'm sorry. I don't know what to say," he finally managed to stutter.

John suddenly changed his demeanor. "Fred," he said kindly. "I've known you a long time, but there is something I really need to know yet. In your letter to this board you mention God and the church several times. What does God and the church really mean to you?"

Fred sat back in the chair, trying to straighten out his befuddled thoughts. Here was a new question. Surely he should be able to answer this one correctly. But Fred was in for a surprise. As he quickly studied over it he suddenly realized that he greatly lacked in this area also. He suddenly became aware that this lack must be apparent, even to those outside the church. Yet, he felt he must somehow rescue himself from this predicament.

"Quite a bit," Fred finally managed to croak.

"Good." John's voice was still kind. "I am a Christian too. I go to church every Sunday and really enjoy participating in any way I can. Do you?"

"Well," Fred squirmed. "I go to church every Sunday, but I don't always participate just the best." He decided he might as well tell it as it was. *It seems John knows all about me anyway.*

"I also like to privately read my Bible and pray every day. Do you?" John quizzed.

Fred thought a moment. "No," he finally admitted.

"Have you been born again?" John asked.

Now Fred squirmed some more. *He is really getting personal now!* "Well, I hope so."

"You *hope* so?!" John reacted in a way that stunned Fred. "I have never heard of such a thing! In my Christian experience you either are or you aren't. Then who *is* the King of your life?"

Fred was speechless. He only shook his head.

John leaned toward Fred and spoke with a firm voice. "Fred, in order to give anyone a "1-O" we need evidence of a deeply held belief; we need evidence of sincerity and consistency. I'm sorry, but we find very little evidence."

Sam sat beside Fred in silence. *I know I am here to give advice if needed, but Fred obviously needed help in this area for years. My advice would seem futile now.*

John looked at Fred's father, the only witness. "Do you have anything to say? You have two minutes to speak your part."

Fred's father had been taking in every word of the proceedings, and he was deeply dismayed. What he had seen and heard hurt him deeply. In fact he was shaken to the core. During the last few moments he realized as he had never realized before—Fred was the product of his home. Fred was as he was, and many of the choices he had made, were because of the influence of his home. And he, his dad, was, to a great degree, responsible.

His mind had been traveling fast. The draft board had been questioning only ten minutes or less, yet they had uncovered years in his mind. *I thought Fred was a good boy. Yes, he has been running around some, but he has never done anything really bad, that I know of. Yet, it is obvious that it looks different to the men of the community. What do they see, and why? They seemed to challenge Fred's nonresistance, carrying it into areas I had never thought about. They even challenged my nonresistance. They really dug in, trying to find out how deep Fred's faith really is. I'm afraid in this case it really is "like father, like son." Oh how I wish I could still change some things!* But deep down he feared it was too late for Fred.

Fred's dad looked at John. "Sir, I'm sorry. I have nothing to say."

Now John looked at Sam. "We don't usually ask the counselor to speak, but I know you are Fred's deacon. Do you have anything to say? Keep it short."

Sam's mind had been racing too. Yes, Fred's answers reflected how he really was. *We suspected it was this way for several years, yes, even when he was taking instruction for baptism. Why didn't we help him? We thought we didn't know for sure, we didn't know how, but Oh!, why did we just let it ride? What can I say now to change it? Nothing. Now it's too late!*

Sam looked up, tears standing in his eyes. "I am very sorry, but I have nothing to offer."

John faced the rest of the board. "Do any of you have any questions or comments?"

They shook their heads.

"This concludes the hearing," John stated matter-of-factly. "Fred, you will be notified of our decision by mail in a day or two. You are dismissed."

The somber group left wordlessly.

Out in the parking lot they gathered around Sam's car. "It is obvious what their decision will be. What do I do now?" Fred asked, his face pale as he faced Deacon Sam.

Sam was unable to talk. He was weeping silently. Finally he regained his composure enough to speak. "Fred, I am very sorry! I feel you are where you are today, at least partly because of my neglect. I am sorry and beg your forgiveness!"

Fred's dad struggled to speak. "Son, I too am very sorry. I saw myself today as I never saw myself before. I have failed to be the Christian I should be. I have not been the father you really needed all these years. Please forgive me!"

Fred was overwhelmed. He struggled to keep his composure, his mind still going in crazy circles. He could hardly comprehend what was really being said. "It's O.K," he answered dully. "But what am I supposed to do now?"

Sam blew his nose before answering, "Well, I guess you probably have three choices. You can appeal the decision, or you can refuse to report for duty and face possible charges. Or, you can report for military duty. Of course, I hope you don't choose military duty."

"What *should* I do?" asked Fred, desperately. "I guess I am so mixed up right now I don't know *what* I want!"

"And I feel so bad about this that I don't feel qualified to advise you," Fred's dad answered.

"I think we need to go home and spend the evening and night praying about this," Sam suggested. "I will use the hotline to ask our congregation to pray. Perhaps by morning we will have an answer on how to proceed."

"O.K." Fred answered meekly as they separated to go home.

That evening in bed, Fred tossed and tossed. Sleep completely eluded him. The question John had asked, "Have you been born again?" kept running through his mind, over and over again. He pondered the question. *I was baptized . . . . but I guess I never gave it much thought. I never was much on reading the Bible and praying. I guess I didn't see much need.*

Then he heard John again. "We find no evidence of a deeply held belief. . . . I think he will make a good soldier." *So what did I say wrong? What did he mean by a deeply held belief? How do I get a deeply held belief? So many questions and no answers.*

All night long Fred tossed and turned, his mind refusing to shut off. Sleep would not come to the disturbed young man. Finally at 4:30 A.M. he turned on the light and dressed. *Somehow, I must do something! I can't go on like this!*

Fred stumbled down the stairs and found a phone.

At Deacon Sam Burkholder's house there was a light on in the study. He had been alone for some time already. His heart was so heavy. *How can I help Fred in this difficult time?*

He had met with the ministry last night. They had discussed the situation and shared their concerns. He too had slept fitfully, and finally rose at 4 A.M. to fall on his knees crying to his Heavenly Father. Now he was seeking direction in the Word.

The phone rang. It was Fred. "Oh, sure, come on over right away," he invited. "I was thinking about you. No, it's O.K, come on over."

A bit later Fred was seated in Sam's study. "I feel terrible! I don't know what to do!"

"Is the military service what is bothering you?"

"Yes," Fred answered quickly. "I don't want to go to the army and help kill people! I couldn't sleep well all night. All I did was toss and turn."

Sam was very solemn. "Fred, I didn't sleep well either. I was also upset about what the draft board said. But I believe my concern is somewhat different from yours at this point."

"What do you mean?" Fred wondered, a puzzled look on his face.

"Well, Fred, it is like this. The draft board questioned you quite sharply. They seemed to know more about you than we did. They obviously have made their decision—they passed judgment on you. It didn't sound good. We didn't like it at all. But there was an air of finality about it, even though we didn't get an official notice yet, and they mentioned the possibility of an appeal."

Fred listened spellbound, even though he had

rehearsed those thoughts dozens of times.

Sam continued. "But, Fred, this is what really burdens my heart. There is another "draft board" coming. The chairman of this "Board" is the King of Kings. He will have no need to ask you any questions—He knows you perfectly. He knows what you have done, and what you have not done. He knows exactly what you are and what you are not. He sees into the depth of your heart."

Sam paused to let the meaning of his words soak in. And from the look on Fred's face the words were having their effect.

"Fred," Sam continued softly. "When He passes judgment it will be right. There will be no mistakes. And the judgment will be for real, and for eternity."

He paused again. His heart went out to the young man in front of him. He looked so totally miserable. "Fred, whatever happens with you concerning this draft situation is only for a short time, even if it may be many years in prison. When the King of Kings passes judgment on your soul, it will be forever."

Fred squirmed in his chair. His mind was filled with new thoughts, but he didn't speak.

"Fred," Sam's voice was pleading. "Let me ask you a question; a very important question. "Will the

King of Kings also say, 'No deeply held faith?' What do you think He will say?"

Fred's mouth did not move, but his mind was racing. *I know what he is saying is true. If I met Jesus today I would not be ready. What a horrible thought! But what can I do? I have no idea . . . .*

Aloud he said, "Yes, He would probably also say, 'No deeply held faith.' And I think He would say, 'Depart from me, I never knew you.'" Fred leaned forward in his chair.

Then it seemed as if the dam broke. Fred lost all control of his pent-up emotions and broke into loud sobs. Sam sat there with tears streaming down his face.

When Fred finally gained control of himself, Sam asked, "Fred have you been praying about this?"

Fred decided to be very open and honest. There was no use keeping anything hid. "No, I have never done much praying; I really don't know how. But I am at the end of my rope; I want to learn—if it's not too late."

Sam Burkholder was shocked beyond words. "Wh-, what do you mean by saying you don't know how to pray? You were baptized!"

"Yes, I know I was baptized, but that was all," Fred

answered. "Yesterday when John asked me if I was 'born again' I hardly knew what to say. Now I know my answer should have been "no.""

Sam sat deep in thought. *I knew Fred seemed "shallow," but I had no idea . . . .*

"I admit I am shocked," Sam finally replied. "But I am glad you are man enough to admit it."

"I know I can't go on like this," Fred moaned. "Is there any hope for me? I mean for me personally; my soul. I guess I hardly know how to say it, but I am not thinking about getting drafted. I need peace in my soul!"

The deacon's eyes lighted. "Fred, yes, there is hope for you. If you are ready and willing to do your part without any reservation. Do you realize you are a vile sinner? Are you ready to confess those sins?"

Fred bowed his head as he contemplated the deacon's words. Then he humbly admitted, "Yes, I realize I am a sinner, but I want to free myself of this terrible weight on my heart. I will tell you all." Fred poured out his sins before Sam. He held nothing back. It seemed he would never finish. One thought led to another, until he finally stopped with, "I guess that is all that I can think of right now."

Sam looked at Fred with new respect and said, "I

know these last ten minutes took a lot of courage. I
believe this was the work of the Holy Spirit. Now,
would you want to kneel down with me and pray? I
would encourage you to pray first, then I will pray.
Is that all right?"

Fred hesitated but for a moment, "Yes, I want to
pray; I feel I must, but I don't know if I can pray out
loud."

"I understand, but perhaps it may be easier if you
think of it this way; praying is talking to God. You
are doing real well in talking to me, and I am the
only one besides God that will hear you when you
pray out loud. The words you say don't need to be
fancy. What you feel in your heart is what matters,
and I believe God is pleased with what He sees in
your heart right now."

Fred pondered Sam's words. He was not easily
convinced. Praying to God seemed like a big thing to
him. And praying out loud was almost more than he
could fathom. *I don't know if I can do it! But somehow,
I must! I can't stop now.*

Aloud he said, "Okay, I want to try."

As they knelt together in that little room, the
house around them was still in slumber. Fred felt
as if he was in a totally foreign land, in completely

unfamiliar territory. He began to pray with halting, stammering words. But gradually he found words to express the longing of his heart. Then Sam prayed.

When they arose from their knees, the tears were dripping from Fred's face, but there was a glint of joy in his eyes. He stared out the window. The early morning sun was casting its first rays of light in the eastern sky, promising the dawn of yet another day. These rays of light portrayed rays of hope to Fred. Hope that Fred had never before experienced.

Another Day—Another Hearing

JIM'S FATHER LOOKED AT his son. He was concerned. The word of Fred's draft board hearing had flown like wild-fire. He had not expected Fred to encounter any problems. Now Jim was going; today, in fact. He reached for a piece of toast. "Jim are you ready for the hearing this forenoon?"

"Yeah," Jim answered calmly between bites. "I dropped my paper work off yesterday morning. They told me to be there at 10 A.M."

"Who is going with you?" Dad questioned.

"No one that I know of."

"Don't you think someone should go along?" Dad was worried now. "Didn't you hear how it went with Fred ? They really gave him a hard time!"

"Dad, you don't know Fred," Jim answered, casually. "Fred just doesn't know how to handle . . . Well, you just let me handle it."

"But, Jim!" Dad countered. "I still think it may be a good idea to have someone with you."

Jim chewed for a while. "Okay," he finally agreed. "You can go with me. But I don't want any preachers along."

At 10 o'clock Jim and his father walked into the hearing room at the local courthouse.

John, the draft board chairman rose to his feet and greeted them. "I am John, the chairman of this board. I guess you know me well. Have a seat." He motioned to the empty chair on the opposite side of the table.

Jim took a seat, and his father stood behind him. Jim looked at the faces of the men on the draft board. He knew several of them. He noticed their faces had a "set" look. But Jim had a plan, and he too was determined.

John looked at Jim. "I see your father is here. I suppose he is your counselor?"

"Yes, sir," Jim answered evenly.

"You know the rules about the counselor?" John questioned.

"Yes," Jim answered again.

"He may be seated beside you."

John picked up a paper from the top of the pile in front of him. "I see you are asking for a CO status, and you listed some Bible verses to back this claim. Jim, we know what you have been doing and how you have been living. And we also know it doesn't even come close to matching what you have written in this letter!"

He mockingly waved the letter in front of Jim's face. "Now, explain to me the difference between what you write and what you live!"

Jim had expected opposition. He was prepared—he thought.

"The Bible says, 'Thou shalt not kill.' And it also says, 'Resist not evil.' So I simply can't go to war."

"Oh! So you believe the Bible?" John sneered.

"Yes, I do," Jim replied trying his utmost to remain calm.

"Well, so do I!" John exclaimed loudly. "My Bible also condemns fornicators. Does yours? Answer me!"

"Y-y-yes, I guess," Jim stammered. The questioning had taken an unexpected turn.

Exasperated with the young man in front of him,

John was red in the face now. "You say you simply cannot go to war because the Bible says so and so. Yet you can go to town and watch X-rated movies. You also buy the dirtiest magazines you can buy, and you keep company with the "loosest" girls in town. To me that means you are probably indulging in sin. Yet you say you simply cannot go to the army because of what the Bible says. Explain *that* to me!"

Suddenly Jim's well-laid plan disappeared. He was left speechless.

John waited a few moments for Jim to answer. Those few moments seemed almost like hours to Jim's father. Finally John resumed.

"So you have nothing to say. I told you what you are doing. Is it true you are doing these things? I demand an answer."

Jim squirmed. "I might have done some of those things," Jim hedged with hanging head.

The draft board stared at Jim with piercing eyes. John cleared his throat. "Then let me ask another question. Was it not only about six months ago that your neighbor decided to build a new line fence between his farm and your father's farm? And was it not you, Jim, that was all riled up because he was building it three feet too far on your father's land? Was it not you that *happened* to meet the local attorney in the coffee shop and asked him what could be done about it? Jim, answer me, is the answer 'yes' to all those questions?"

Jim cleared his throat then meekly admitted, "Yes, I guess so."

"And is this the way you would define nonresistance in practice?" John challenged.

Jim felt completely defeated. He gave no answer.

John turned to the other board members. They had been silent all this time, and now they nodded their heads to John's questioning look.

"Jim," John spoke clearly but grimly. "You will be notified in a day or two of our decision. But I will tell you this much. Your belief seems very shallow to us. You are dismissed."

Jim and his father meekly left the room, and wordlessly got in the car and headed towards home. The trip was made in silence.

• • • • • • • •

Sam walked up the steps to the house where Fred

lived with his parents. A knock on the door brought Fred's mother to the door. "Oh, come in," she greeted, smiling warmly. "Would you like to see Fred?"

"Yes," Sam answered. "If he is available."

"Oh, yes, he is here. I'll call him."

Fred and Sam settled into chairs around the kitchen table. "Fred," Sam began. "What have you got in mind to do about the draft?"

Fred didn't answer. Staring into space, he sat opposite the older man, deep in thought. Finally he stirred. "I don't know that I have much choice. I don't think I have a chance to win an appeal. I cannot make myself go to the Army. I suppose they may put me in prison."

Sam had been studying Fred closely. "Why don't you try to appeal? I don't know if there is any chance, but I would be willing to do what I can to help."

Fred's face brightened, then fell as he asked, "Would that be nonresistant to go to court to try to change their decision?"

Sam thought a moment. "I see your point. And I am glad to see that you are sensitive about that. But if I understand this right, you would not be demanding anything, you would only be asking the draft board to reconsider your case."

"I don't know, it seems so hopeless and useless. Why go through all that again?"

"Yes, it does seem hopeless to you, but perhaps God has something else in mind," Sam encouraged.

"What does Joseph think of making an appeal?" Fred asked. "Have you talked this over with him?"

"Yes, I have," Sam stated. "In fact it was his idea that I come and suggest this to you."

"I really see no use in it, but if you two both think so, I will do it," Fred answered. "Is that what those papers are about?" He motioned towards the papers in Sam's hands.

Sam shifted his papers. "Yes, it is. Here is a blank sheet of paper, all you need to do is write a short note to the District Appeal Board requesting an appeal."

Sam helped Fred compose the short note, and Fred signed it.

"I will take this to them today, and they will probably notify you by mail when the hearing is scheduled. If they choose to deny again, we can appeal to the National Appeal Board if we want to," Sam said as he gathered his things together.

"I really dread going through that again," Fred said.

"I know, but this time we will feel free to give

you the support you need. Remember, nothing is impossible with God."

The Draft Board Decides

ED GLANCED AROUND THE room, his eyes taking it all in. Bishop Joseph Hostetler, Minister Chester King and Deacon Sam Burkholder were all seated around the long kitchen table. Joining them were Dad and Mom, and himself. Standing around the table with concerned interest were the rest of the family. The sight melted Ed's heart. He knew they all loved him; he could see it shine in every action.

"Ed, did you get your forms filled out and your letter written?" Sam asked, bringing all the minds in the room into focus.

"Yes," Ed answered. "And Chester helped a lot with corrections in my grammar. And he also made some very good suggestions on how to word some of my thoughts more clearly." He smiled slightly in the minister's direction.

"I would like to say something first before we go further in this," Joseph interrupted kindly. "I think we all feel a need of God's presence and guidance. Let's kneel in prayer before we go further."

They all fell to their knees and Joseph led in fervent prayer.

After they were seated again and composed, Joseph turned to Sam, "Please proceed as you think best."

"Perhaps we could start with reading your statement of faith if you don't mind, Ed," Sam began.

"Sure," said Ed as he handed the paper over to Sam. To himself he thought, *This is so embarrassing! But I guess they are really trying to help.*

Sam read the hand-written statement from start to finish. Ed waited expectantly for their reaction.

Joseph was the first to speak. "Ed, if you had written this a year ago I would not have believed it. Now, I want to ask you a very personal question. You say in this statement that Jesus is now the Lord of your life, and you cannot deny Him by taking up arms. Are you ready to suffer persecution, prison, or even death rather than taking up arms?"

Ed was stunned at the forthrightness of the

question, yet it was not a new thought. Joseph somehow brought it into new light. Suddenly the possibility seemed so real!

Ed bowed his head, the tears coming to his eyes. "Yes, by the grace of God, I am. Or, should I say, I want to be that way. I feel weak at times, but that is what I really want—to be faithful, whatever it costs."

"Is there any way we can help you?" Chester questioned.

"I really feel the prayers of the church. Don't stop praying," Ed answered.

Bishop Joseph Hostetler had been thinking. "Ed, two of the others have faced the same board you will face tomorrow. In both cases they seemed to know a lot about the boys they were questioning. As you know, in both cases they passed judgment by giving a 1-A. I hate to admit it, but, in both cases they probably judged right."

"By the way," Chester injected. "Did you hear that Jim left today? He's joining the Army. He says he has no other choice."

Everyone was stunned into silence.

"How sad, how terribly sad!" Joseph was the first to find his voice.

Ed found his tongue next. "I am not surprised. I am just sorry I didn't try harder to help him."

"I feel the same," Sam answered weakly.

"We feel a terrible loss," Joseph started in again. "And we should feel it. Yet, I am concerned that we don't become paralyzed by the loss of one member in a way that we suffer even more losses. Is there something we should have done that we are not doing for Ed?"

"As far as the draft board is concerned, yes, I think Ed needs to approach this differently," Sam spoke up. "I think they already know enough about Ed's past that they will probably try to capitalize on that, just as they did on the others. It is my opinion that Ed may as well confess his past to them as soon as he has the opportunity."

"I don't feel like defending myself one bit," put in Ed.

"We also have a written testimony that Bob Jerger wrote, and one that I wrote myself," Sam stated. "I delivered a copy of both of them to the Draft Board today so they will have time to review them before the hearing."

"That is good," responded Joseph. "I am so thankful for Bob Jerger's cooperation in this. I see this as a big help."

The rest of the evening was spent in counseling and encouraging each other with the Word of God.

As he was leaving Joseph laid his hand on Ed's shoulder. "Ed, only God knows what He has in store for you, but we know He will be with you whatever may come."

"Thanks," said Ed, huskily.

The next morning a group of men stood waiting outside the room where the draft board was already assembled. They could hear the muffled sound of voices inside the closed doors. Ed noticed the voices. *They have probably read my papers and are discussing my case.* He glanced at the men that had come with him. They were Joseph Hostetler, Sam Burkholder, his father, and Bob Jerger. Ed especially noticed the concerned look on Bob's face. Bob had readily agreed to come along and had promised to do all he could to help him.

The door to the hearing room creaked loudly, and slowly swung open. The secretary smiled. "Are you Edward Martin?"

"Yes, sir, I am," answered Ed.

"Come in and be seated," she said, motioning him to a chair.

Ed sat in the chair at the table, noticing the draft board on the opposite side. Joseph took the chair at Ed's side. Ed's father and Bob stood just inside the door by the wall. Sam waited outside.

"I guess by now you all know how we operate," John stated.

"Yes," Ed answered as he studied John. *John is sure different here. Where has his friendliness gone?*

"We have studied and discussed your paperwork," John said as his piercing eyes almost drilled holes into Ed. "Now tell me, why do you think you should be given a 1-O?"

Ed was silent for a brief moment, praying silently to God for wisdom. Then he felt a calmness creep over him. "Sir, I know you have lots of reasons not to give me what I am asking for. I have lived the life of a hypocrite and a terrible sinner. But I have repented, and I have done my best to make restitution. My life has changed, yet I realize you probably know much better how I used to be than how I am now. I am sorry for my past. I don't want to live that kind of life any more; I want to live for my Redeemer, by the grace of God. I believe that Jesus Christ taught the way of non-resistance. I want to live as He taught."

The draft board sat in silence as Ed paused. "If

you must give me a 1-A, I will try to accept that without an argument, but there is no way possible that I can serve in the military. I will try my best to pay the fine and serve my prison sentence as God gives me the grace."

John was visibly moved. When he finally spoke he directed his question to Joseph who was sitting at Ed's side. "Is it true that Ed has changed?"

Joseph cleared his throat. "Yes," he answered clearly. "There is no doubt on my part; Ed has had a real Damascus road experience. He is a different young man today."

"And when was this change?" John asked, looking at the bishop.

"About six months ago."

Now one of the other draft board members spoke up, pointing at Ed's father. "Is Ed's story true?"

Ed's father spoke slowly and sincerely. "Yes, it is true."

"Bob Jerger, what have you got to say about this?" John turned to the Auto Parts man.

Bob straightened his long, lanky frame. "I have known this young man since he was a small boy tagging his daddy. I have been involved with this family in business and as a friend for years. I have observed Ed during the last few years; I know it is true that he strayed. It seemed to me I realized it more than his dad, but I also know that Ed has made a definite change in the last months."

The room was silent for a moment. It seemed the draft board was trying to gather their scattered thoughts together. Finally John looked at Ed again. "Ed, do you admit that your belief in God, your nonresistant faith was something that was not deeply held, that it was all a front; a sham?"

"Yes," replied Ed evenly. "I was not fit to be called a conscientious objector, and if you decide to let me serve my time in alternative service it will be as an act of mercy."

John looked at the other draft board members. One of them leaned over speaking in low tones.

"Ed," John began. "Your dad has some fat cattle in the lot close by the barn. Let's say that tonight some one comes and shoots the best steer you have; helps himself to your tractor and loader to load the steer, then takes it home to put it in his freezer. You see it all happen. What will you do?"

Ed studied, his mind racing. *I know what I would have done before . . .but, what would I do now? I know what I should do, but just what would I really do?*

"Sir," he answered carefully. "I must be honest with you. I really don't know what I would do. I know what Jesus said, 'If someone take thy coat, give him thy cloak also.' That is what I should do, and what I would want to do, but I know my weakness. When we are put to the test it would be harder than we realize."

"What if those men came back every day for a while?" questioned John. "Would that make a difference?"

"It should not." Ed answered. "It would be hard, but God's grace was sufficient for the apostle Paul. I know it would be for me too."

John looked at the other board members with a questioning look. They all shrugged their shoulders.

"You are all dismissed," John stated, looking at Ed. "The secretary will mail your paperwork to you in a few days."

Ed rose to his feet and they all filed out the door.

Outside the courthouse the group gathered around Ed. The strange calm feeling that Ed had during the hearing was now gone. Ed's hands were shaking so badly he could hardly hold still.

"I wouldn't be surprised if you get your notice in the mail tomorrow," Sam was saying. It is only 9:30

now. They could easily get it in the mail yet today."

"I watched the draft board closely," Joseph commented. "I really couldn't tell what they were thinking. It almost seemed like they didn't know what to think; maybe they are trying to make a decision right now. I think we should pray."

The group, standing at the side of Ed's father's car, bowed their heads, praying to their Almighty God as their bishop led them in prayer.

Lifting their heads, they replaced their headgear.

Joseph spoke calmly, "Now there is nothing for us to do but go home and lay this matter in God's hands, trusting that He will give us the grace to accept the outcome, whatever He sees best."

Ed got into the car, his mind and emotions in a whirl. *How . . . what . . .yet, Thank You, Lord!*

The following day found Ed trying to concentrate on the pickup truck he was servicing. It was hard with his mind going back to yesterday's hearing. *Why did I say . . . Why didn't I say . . . Just what did they really think? Will mail-time ever get here? It is still an hour. . . .*

Ed's eyes continually returned to the window that faced the road—and the mailbox. Now he looked again—just in time to see the tail end of a car disappear into their lane. *Who is that?*

Ed's answer came in a few moments when the door opened and Joseph and Sam walked in.

Ed looked up with a welcoming smile. "Hello, come on in! I'm just trying to concentrate on my work." He grinned, trying to relieve the tension that had been building up inside him all morning.

"We thought we would try to be here when your mail arrives today," greeted Joseph. "We didn't know for sure just when the mail comes here, so we thought we would come early."

"We are glad you came," Dad returned walking up to the two men. "Your support at this time is greatly appreciated."

They soon were busy in conversation and time passed more quickly. Suddenly the mailman was spotted at the mailbox.

Ed ran for the mail box, but this time he remembered to watch for cars as he crossed the road. He shuddered when he thought how nearly he had been hit.

Opening the box, he shuffled through the pile of letters. Sure enough, there was an official looking letter that looked like the one they were looking for. He grabbed the mail and headed for the shop.

"Here it is, I'll let you open it," Ed puffed as he handed the letter to his bishop. "I don't think I have the courage to open it." His heart was pounding; partly from running and partly from anxiety.

Joseph took the letter, then reached into his pocket for his pocket-knife. With one deft stroke he slit it open.

The letterhead stood out boldly. Ed could see it from where he stood.

SELECTIVE SERVICE SYSTEM
NOTICE OF CLASSIFICATION

Joseph started reading on the top, "Part 1 is a summary of classification action. On the left side there are boxes with the different classifications. The box "1-O" has an X in it. On the top it says "Decisions." Below that it says "Grant" and "Deny." The box under "Grant" has an X in it."

An emotional thrill went through Ed's heart. There was a pause as Joseph studied the form. "It looks like there were two people that voted to grant and one voted to deny. Down at the bottom it says, "Your present classification is 1-O,"" he finished.

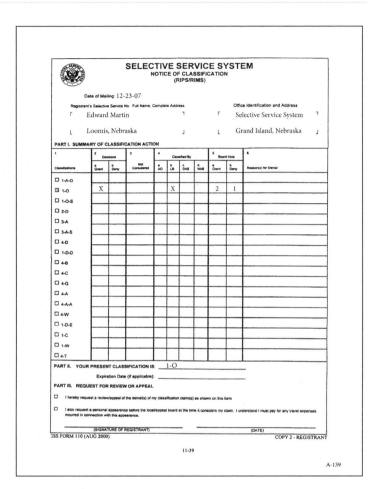

The silence was suddenly broken by Ed. "I feel so unworthy of this!" Then he turned away as his emotions overcame him and he wept silently. All the emotions of the last several weeks seemed to pile on top of him.

Finally Joseph spoke. "I think we owe a prayer of gratitude to God. Let's bow our heads for a word of prayer." The small group of men with bowed heads, thanked the Lord for his great mercy.

As they raised their heads, a customer walked into the repair shop. Looking around the group with sober faces, he must have wondered what had happened.

"What's next in line for me?" Ed wondered as his dad took care of the customer.

"You will probably get a "SSS" form 155, which is an 'Order to perform Alternative Service Form'," answered Sam Burkholder. "But in the mean time you should probably decide where you want to serve. I guess we as the ministry hope you choose a Conservative Anabaptist Service Program (C.A.S.P.) unit. Our churches are preparing a base with the U.S. Forestry Service in Missouri."

"How long will it be before I need to go? Will I have a week or so at home yet?" Ed wondered.

"Yes, probably at least that much," answered Sam. "It may be even longer."

"As far as where I serve, right now anywhere seems much better than the prison I was envisioning. But I think I would like forestry work, if that is what my parents and the ministry think I should do."

"I would be pleased to have you work with other young men from our type churches," Joseph joined in. "But perhaps that part can be discussed later. Now I suspect your family in the house will be happy to have you tell them your good news."

As Ed left for the house, Joseph and Sam walked together towards their car.

"I have been doing some thinking," Joseph began as they started out the lane. "It is obvious by now that our government is very selective in who they allow to be classified as a CO."

"They certainly are," replied Sam. "But, wouldn't you agree that so far they have been correct in their decisions?"

Joseph was silent. It was obvious something was heavy on his mind. Sam waited, knowing he had something more to say.

"Yes, they probably were correct in their decision; more correct than we like to admit. It seems they are very discerning on how deep the faith of our youth really is. They notice inconsistencies even more than we do in some areas." Joseph scratched his head as he pondered his next words.

"It is obvious that our government is insisting on a deeply held faith and consistent practice to qualify for a CO classification. The question that is burning in my mind is this. Should the church be any less discerning? Should we be any less insisting on these qualities for church membership?"

"I have pondered that question many times since these hearings have come up," answered Sam slowly. "Especially since our young men have been asked these personal questions."

Joseph spoke as he drove. "Let's pray about this in the coming days. Perhaps we too have been too lax in some ways."

Induction

A WEEK LATER ED entered the house for the noon meal. His mother met him at the door. "It looks like you have an important letter, Ed."

Ed took the letter from her and quickly slit it open with his pocketknife. He drew the contents from the envelope. This is what he saw:

Selective Service System
Order to Perform Alternative Service

Also enclosed were an Alternative Service Worker Guide and a skills questionnaire.

"I wonder what this questionnaire means?" Ed looked puzzled.

Local Board/Area Office
Street Address
City, State, ZIP

SELECTIVE SERVICE SYSTEM
ORDER TO PERFORM ALTERNATIVE SERVICE
(RIPS/RIMS)

Date of Issuance: 1-04-08

Registrant's Name and SSN   Edward Martin   Social Security Number
Street Address   Random Sequence Number 14
City, State, Zip   Loomis, Nebraska

This is your Order to Perform Alternative Service in lieu of induction into the Armed Forces of the United States.

You have been reclassified 1-W (Conscientious Objector ordered to perform alternative service). Under the authority of the Military Selective Service Act you are ordered to perform alternative service for _24_ consecutive months, to begin on the date to be determined by the Director.

Your performance of alternative service will be monitored by the Alternative Service Office (ASO) located at:
_____Grand Island, Nebraska_____, which will contact you in the near future to schedule a job counseling session and assist you in locating a suitable job. During your performance of alternative service, any contact with the Selective Service System should be with the ASO having jurisdictional responsibility for you.

Enclosed is an Alternative Service Worker Guide, which provides general information about the type of work you will perform. Also enclosed is a Skills Questionnaire (SSS Form 156) which asks for information to assist the ASO in placing you in an alternative service job. Please complete and return the SSS Form 156 as soon as your job counseling session is scheduled.

If you are a student pursuing a full-time course of instruction at a high school, college or similar institution of learning, have the enclosed SSS Form 109 (Student Certificate) completed and signed by an authorized school official. The SSS Form 109 must be returned to the Area Office shown above within 10 days from the date of this Order.

John Fortune
(SIGNATURE)   LOCAL BOARD MEMBER

John Fortune
PRINTED NAME

Warning: If you fail to follow the directions in this Order, you may be reported as a suspected violator of the Military Selective Service Act and, if convicted, be subject to imprisonment for up to five years, a fine of up to $250,000, or both.

SSS FORM 155 (AUG 2000)   ORIGINAL

11-60

Dad looked over his shoulder, scanning the contents. "Maybe we'd better get our meal eaten then we can concentrate on studying it some more."

As the family settled into their respective places at the table, Ed glanced around the table. *I feel so at home here—do I really have to leave?*

His father led in asking the blessing on the meal.

Soon the table resounded with pleasant sounds. Dishes and utensils clattered as everyone tried to talk at once. The letter from the SSS was foremost in everyone's mind.

"What does that letter mean—order to perform?" Mom voiced her concern.

"I don't hardly know myself, but I guess it is saying this is my notice that I am now drafted," Ed replied. "But it doesn't say where, or when."

"I think we will take the letter to our deacon right after dinner," Dad announced. "He seems to understand all this much better than we do."

Ed and his father found Sam behind the barn. Ed handed him the letter and asked, "What do you make of this?"

Sam looked it over. "This is basically your notice that you will need to serve 24 months of alternative service."

"But what does this Skills Questionnaire mean?" Ed asked. "Do I need to fill that all out?"

"I don't think so," Sam answered. "That is for the ones that are depending on SSS to find them Alternative Service employment. The Skills Questionnaire helps them determine what type of job you are suited for. This probably doesn't apply to you since you already know where you want to go. There should be a place. . . Hm.-"

"That's a relief," interrupted Ed, reading over Sam's shoulder.

"Oh, here it is," said Sam. "Here at the back there is a section called *Proposed Alternative Service Job*. If you want to serve in the C.A.S.P unit you will need to fill this out, but probably not the rest."

"That is what I want," Ed answered readily. "Would you help me fill it out?"

"Sure," Sam replied. "Let's do it right now." He led the way over to the office in his shop.

The next day the mailman carried Ed's reply on its way.

• • • • • • • •

Three weeks later Ed stood beside his car with the door open and the car running. His whole family clustered around him, ready to see him off.

"How far is it to Winona, Missouri?" his older sister asked.

"Right around 520 miles," Ed answered. "I should

be there well before dark, Lord willing."

Ed's eyes misted as he looked at his family. "I will miss you all," he continued, "but, I feel a bit strange. I've dreaded this for so long. The thought of being called by the SSS used to fill me with dread and fear. Now I am about to leave to answer that call, and I feel at peace. In fact, I feel privileged to be able to serve in this way."

"Ed," his father started in. "We are sad to see you leave, yet we are so glad it is this and not a prison stay. That makes it so much easier to part. But the best part is that we can rejoice in your faithfulness. We pray that you will remain faithful to the end."

"Thank you, Dad, and all of you." Ed answered huskily. "I must be going."

Quietly Dad spoke up again, "Son you are answering the call of the SSS. But let's remember, we all want to be ready to answer the most important call of all, the call of the King of Kings!"